# MY CAMINO JOURNAL

## DAYS IN THE LIFE OF A PILGRIM

CREATED BY
### HEATHER GAILEY

AMBERHORN
LIVONIA, MICHIGAN

# MY CAMINO JOURNAL

Published by Amber Horn
an imprint of BHC Press

Library of Congress Control Number:
2017952178

ISBN-13: 978-1-946848-91-8


Visit the publisher at:
www.bhcpress.com

Thank You
to all the Dragonflies in my life.
Without you, I would never have learned to fly.

## ABOUT THE JOURNAL

In the Fall of 2015, and after a long 25 years of daydreaming and talking about the Camino to anyone who would listen, I finalized my plans and set out at the age of 52 to walk the Camino Frances, solo. My friends and family thought I had lost my mind, but I knew deep down that I had actually found it. My spiritual journey turned out to be very different than I had originally planned, but it was still a life altering adventure that challenged me physically, spiritually, and mentally. I took my first step onto the Camino from a city in the middle (a story for another time), and made my way to the end in 17 days without even officially finishing and collecting the highly sought after Compostela (certificate of completion) due to time constraints.

If you are a Camino "newbie" I am here to pass on to you that the Camino de Santiago has the power to throw you up in the air, flip you upside down and then dump you on your head. It will then turn around and show kindness by picking you up, dusting you off, and staying with you until you find your centre. All this will happen just in time for you to return home. Trust me! It happened to me. If you are someone who has been before then you will know exactly what I mean.

Whether this is your first Camino or your 20th, it is important to remember that your Camino is your Camino. You will meet people along the way who will remind you of this when you feel things are not going the way you had planned or expected. There are also those who will attempt to judge you, but remember, there is no wrong way to complete it. It is important for you to document your journey. Why? Because I say so! Now go...

# MORE ABOUT THE JOURNAL

Now, as you hold this nubbin of gold in your hot little hands, I would like to say WELCOME to the *My Camino Journal*. As I have mentioned, I believe whole-heartedly in journaling and I want to take this opportunity to get you addicted to the benefits journaling can offer you, especially for a trip like the Camino.

When you keep a journal, you open yourself up to self-discovery, reflection, healing, and personal growth. A journal can also be a safe space to capture your life story, provide a place for photo information, and can serve as a record of important personal milestones, triumphs, and lessons.

I created this journal for those who love to journal and for those who do not. This journal will allow you to put as much or as little effort into the process as you desire. It is fun and irreverent, spiritual yet not overtly religious, and provides a daily structure for those who admit to having an adverse reaction to the ominous nature of the blank page.

My wish is that you will enjoy using this journal so much that you will decide to buy one for each of your friends and family members, who will then decide to set out on their own Camino journey after hearing all about your awesome adventure.

## WRITE YOUR OWN STORY!

## INSTRUCTIONS

The *My Camino Journal* allows for a total of 36 days of journal entries. Each day has four pages to complete. Follow the wandering boot prints as they walk you through creating your unique story.

1) **My Camino**: A page where you can log the distances traveled, steps taken, the weather, your feelings, places you stayed, the money you spent, the types of food eaten, and your mode of transportation.

2) **My Purpose**: A contemplative practice to implement as you prepare to walk. Ask yourself these three important questions each morning, knowing that the answers will guide your actions for the entire day.

The questions are simple yet meaningful:
1) What is my purpose today?
2) Who am I supposed to help?
3) Who is supposed to help me?

3) **My Thoughts**: A daily quote about walking, offering a prompt to consider throughout the day, ruminate on later or share with others.

4) **Mindfulness Minute**: A place to reflect or have some fun, depending on the day.

This page will self-destruct now that you are finished reading it.

# 5! 4! 3! 2! 1!

# AND SO IT BEGINS...

Your story. A journey of a lifetime.
Take a moment to remember what your life was like
yesterday, because after you lay one foot on
The Camino,

your life will NEVER be the same.

## BUEN CAMINO

This very important Journal belongs to:

_____

If this **AWESOME** account of my life changing trip is ever lost, and you happen to find it, please return it to:

_____

_____

_____

# DAY 1

# DAY 1 - MY CAMINO

From: _____ to: _____

The weather is:                I am feeling:

☼  ☁  ☁  🌧  🌨        ☺  😄  😐  😣  😴

➡ ➡ ➡ ➡ ➡ ➡ ➡ ➡ ➡ ➡ ➡ ➡ ➡ ➡

Total distance traveled: ___ KMs ☐ Miles ☐ Inches ☐

Walked ☐ Cycled ☐ Taxi ☐ Bus ☐ Plane ☐ Horse ☐
Other ☐ _____

➡ ➡ ➡ ➡ ➡ ➡ ➡ ➡ ➡ ➡ ➡ ➡ ➡ ➡

Stayed @: _____

Albergue ☐ Hostel ☐ Hotel ☐ Tent ☐ Under the stars ☐

➡ ➡ ➡ ➡ ➡ ➡ ➡ ➡ ➡ ➡ ➡ ➡ ➡ ➡

Ate:  Breakfast ☐ _____

            Eat it again! ☐  So So ☐  Bleck ☐
        Lunch ☐ _____

            Eat it again! ☐  So So ☐  Bleck ☐
        Dinner ☐ _____

            Eat it again! ☐  So So ☐  Bleck ☐

Spent: _____ Euros ☐  Dollars ☐  Other ☐
On lodgings ☐  On food ☐  On Gifts ☐  Other ☐

➡ ➡ ➡ ➡ ➡ ➡ ➡ ➡ ➡ ➡ ➡ ➡ ➡ ➡

Tomorrow is a new day. Important things to remember:

_____

_____

_____

# DAY 1 - MY PURPOSE

What is my purpose today? ♡

_____

_____

_____

Who am I to help? 🤝 With what?

_____

_____

_____

Who will help me? 🤝 With what?

_____

_____

_____

Lessons learned along The Way
Gifts from the Universe/GOD/Angels/Spirits

**1** _____

**2** _____

**3** _____

What piece of equipment am I most grateful for today?

_____

Angels (Pilgrims) I met on the Camino today:

Name: _____

Contact info: _____

Name: _____

Contact info: _____

No one saves us but ourselves. No one can and no one may.
We ourselves must walk the path.
- Buddha -

_____

_____

_____

_____

_____

_____

_____

_____

_____

_____

## DAY 1 - MINDFULNESS MINUTE

Reflect and Go Deep:
Why have I chosen this Camino journey?

_____

_____

_____

_____

_____

_____

_____

_____

_____

People will ask you this question over, and over,
and over. So now would be a good time
to get your story straight!

# DAY 2

# DAY 2 - MY CAMINO

From: _____ to: _____

The weather is:                I am feeling:

☀ ☁ ⛅ 🌧 🌨          ☺ 😄 😐 😣 😴

➡ ➡ ➡ ➡ ➡ ➡ ➡ ➡ ➡ ➡ ➡ ➡ ➡

Total distance traveled: ___ KMs ☐ Miles ☐ Inches ☐

Walked ☐ Cycled ☐ Taxi ☐ Bus ☐ Plane ☐ Horse ☐
Other ☐ _____

➡ ➡ ➡ ➡ ➡ ➡ ➡ ➡ ➡ ➡ ➡ ➡ ➡

Stayed @: _____

Albergue ☐ Hostel ☐ Hotel ☐ Tent ☐ Under the stars ☐

➡ ➡ ➡ ➡ ➡ ➡ ➡ ➡ ➡ ➡ ➡ ➡ ➡

Ate: Breakfast ☐ _____

             Eat it again! ☐ So So ☐ Bleck ☐

       Lunch ☐ _____

             Eat it again! ☐ So So ☐ Bleck ☐

      Dinner ☐ _____

             Eat it again! ☐ So So ☐ Bleck ☐

Spent: _____ Euros ☐ Dollars ☐ Other ☐
On lodgings ☐ On food ☐ On Gifts ☐ Other ☐

➡ ➡ ➡ ➡ ➡ ➡ ➡ ➡ ➡ ➡ ➡ ➡ ➡

Tomorrow is a new day. Important things to remember:

_____

_____

_____

What is my purpose today? ♡

_____
_____
_____

Who am I to help? 🤝 With what?

_____
_____
_____

Who will help me? 🤝 With what?

_____
_____
_____

Lessons learned along The Way
Gifts from the Universe/GOD/Angels/Spirits

**1** _____

**2** _____

**3** _____

What piece of equipment am I most grateful for today?

_____

Angels (Pilgrims) I met on the Camino today:

Name: _____

Contact info: _____

Name: _____

Contact info: _____

# DAY 2 - MY THOUGHTS

Walk as if you are kissing the earth with your feet.
- Thich Nhat Hanh -

_____

_____

_____

_____

_____

_____

_____

_____

_____

_____

_____

_____

# DAY 2 - MINDFULNESS MINUTE

Questions:
How am I feeling about my decision to walk?

_____

_____

_____

_____

_____

_____

_____

_____

_____

_____

After my first full day of walking
I said out loud "what was I thinking?!"
I also felt as if I wanted to die. How about you?

# DAY 3

# DAY 3 - MY CAMINO

From: _____ to: _____

The weather is:                    I am feeling:

☼  ☁  ⛅  🌧  ❄          ☺  😀  😐  😣  😴

➡ ➡ ➡ ➡ ➡ ➡ ➡ ➡ ➡ ➡ ➡ ➡ ➡ ➡

Total distance traveled: ___ KMs ☐ Miles ☐ Inches ☐

Walked ☐ Cycled ☐ Taxi ☐ Bus ☐ Plane ☐ Horse ☐
Other ☐ _____

➡ ➡ ➡ ➡ ➡ ➡ ➡ ➡ ➡ ➡ ➡ ➡ ➡ ➡

Stayed @: _____

Albergue ☐ Hostel ☐ Hotel ☐ Tent ☐ Under the stars ☐

➡ ➡ ➡ ➡ ➡ ➡ ➡ ➡ ➡ ➡ ➡ ➡ ➡ ➡

Ate:  Breakfast ☐ _____

                   Eat it again! ☐  So So ☐  Bleck ☐

       Lunch ☐ _____

                   Eat it again! ☐  So So ☐  Bleck ☐

      Dinner ☐ _____

                   Eat it again! ☐  So So ☐  Bleck ☐

Spent: _____ Euros ☐   Dollars ☐  Other ☐
On lodgings ☐ On food ☐ On Gifts ☐  Other ☐

➡ ➡ ➡ ➡ ➡ ➡ ➡ ➡ ➡ ➡ ➡ ➡ ➡

Tomorrow is a new day. Important things to remember:

_____

_____

_____

# DAY 3 - MY PURPOSE

What is my purpose today? ♡

_____
_____
_____

Who am I to help? 🤝 With what?

_____
_____
_____

Who will help me? 🤝 With what?

_____
_____
_____

Lessons learned along The Way
Gifts from the Universe/GOD/Angels/Spirits

**1** _____

**2** _____

**3** _____

What piece of equipment am I most grateful for today?

_____

Angels (Pilgrims) I met on the Camino today:

Name: _____

Contact info: _____

Name: _____

Contact info: _____

# DAY 3 - MY THOUGHTS

An early Morning walk is a blessing for the whole day.
- Henry David Thoreau -

_____

_____

_____

_____

_____

_____

_____

_____

_____

_____

_____

## DAY 3 - MINDFULNESS MINUTE

Art Project: Save the empty sugar packets from every café you visit. After you finish each café con leche, tape, or staple all of the sugar packets here! The more, the merrier!

Come back to this page to report what town
or city made the best coffee?

# DAY 4

# DAY 4 - MY CAMINO

From: _____ to: _____

The weather is:                    I am feeling:

☀ ☁ ⛅ 🌧 🌨         ☺ 😄 😐 😣 😴

➡ ➡ ➡ ➡ ➡ ➡ ➡ ➡ ➡ ➡ ➡ ➡ ➡

Total distance traveled: ___ KMs ☐ Miles ☐ Inches ☐

Walked ☐ Cycled ☐ Taxi ☐ Bus ☐ Plane ☐ Horse ☐
Other ☐ _____

➡ ➡ ➡ ➡ ➡ ➡ ➡ ➡ ➡ ➡ ➡ ➡ ➡

Stayed @: _____

Albergue ☐ Hostel ☐ Hotel ☐ Tent ☐ Under the stars ☐

➡ ➡ ➡ ➡ ➡ ➡ ➡ ➡ ➡ ➡ ➡ ➡ ➡

Ate: Breakfast ☐ _____

              Eat it again! ☐  So So ☐  Bleck ☐
       Lunch ☐ _____

              Eat it again! ☐  So So ☐  Bleck ☐
      Dinner ☐ _____

              Eat it again! ☐  So So ☐  Bleck ☐

Spent: _____ Euros ☐   Dollars ☐  Other ☐
On lodgings ☐  On food ☐  On Gifts ☐  Other ☐

➡ ➡ ➡ ➡ ➡ ➡ ➡ ➡ ➡ ➡ ➡ ➡ ➡

Tomorrow is a new day. Important things to remember:

_____

_____

_____

## DAY 4 - MY PURPOSE

What is my purpose today? ♡

_____

_____

_____

Who am I to help? 🤝 With what?

_____

_____

_____

Who will help me? 🤝 With what?

_____

_____

_____

Lessons learned along The Way
Gifts from the Universe/GOD/Angels/Spirits

**1** _____

**2** _____

**3** _____

What piece of equipment am I most grateful for today?

_____

Angels (Pilgrims) I met on the Camino today:

Name: _____

Contact info: _____

Name: _____

Contact info: _____

# DAY 4 - MY THOUGHTS

If we are facing the right direction, all we have to do
is keep on walking.

- Zen Proverbs -

_____

_____

_____

_____

_____

_____

_____

_____

_____

_____

# DAY 4 - MINDFULNESS MINUTE

One Minute Rant: This is your only chance to rant about people who SNORE. Once the space is filled up, there will be no more ranting about SNORING allowed.

_____

_____

_____

_____

_____

_____

_____

_____

_____

Find a farmacia & buy a good set of ear plugs!

# DAY 5

# DAY 5 - MY CAMINO

From: _____ to: _____

The weather is:                I am feeling:

☀ ☁ ⛅ 🌧 🌨            ☺ 😀 😐 😫 😴

➡ ➡ ➡ ➡ ➡ ➡ ➡ ➡ ➡ ➡ ➡ ➡ ➡

Total distance traveled: ___ KMs ☐ Miles ☐ Inches ☐

Walked ☐ Cycled ☐ Taxi ☐ Bus ☐ Plane ☐ Horse ☐
Other ☐ _____

➡ ➡ ➡ ➡ ➡ ➡ ➡ ➡ ➡ ➡ ➡ ➡ ➡

Stayed @: _____

Albergue ☐ Hostel ☐ Hotel ☐ Tent ☐ Under the stars ☐

➡ ➡ ➡ ➡ ➡ ➡ ➡ ➡ ➡ ➡ ➡ ➡ ➡

Ate: Breakfast ☐ _____

                Eat it again! ☐  So So ☐  Bleck ☐
        Lunch ☐ _____

                Eat it again! ☐  So So ☐  Bleck ☐
       Dinner ☐ _____

                Eat it again! ☐  So So ☐  Bleck ☐

Spent: _____ Euros ☐  Dollars ☐  Other ☐
On lodgings ☐  On food ☐  On Gifts ☐  Other ☐

➡ ➡ ➡ ➡ ➡ ➡ ➡ ➡ ➡ ➡ ➡ ➡ ➡

Tomorrow is a new day. Important things to remember:

_____

_____

_____

# DAY 5 - MY PURPOSE

What is my purpose today? ♡

_____
_____
_____

Who am I to help? 🤝 With what?

_____
_____
_____

Who will help me? 🤝 With what?

_____
_____
_____

Lessons learned along The Way
Gifts from the Universe/GOD/Angels/Spirits

**1** _____

**2** _____

**3** _____

What piece of equipment am I most grateful for today?

_____

Angels (Pilgrims) I met on the Camino today:

Name: _____

Contact info: _____

Name: _____

Contact info: _____

Thoughts come clearly while one walks.
- Thomas Mann -

_____

_____

_____

_____

_____

_____

_____

_____

_____

_____

_____

# DAY 5 - MINDFULNESS MINUTE

Take a Rest: Take a load off your tired feet. Have a coffee, spill it, and make some rings. Then write down how you are feeling at this exact moment.

_____

_____

_____

_____

_____

_____

_____

_____

_____

Use the stream of conscious style. You will not be graded on your sentence structure.

# DAY 6

# DAY 6 - MY CAMINO

From: _____ to: _____

The weather is:                I am feeling:

☀ ☁ ⛅ 🌧 ❄        ☺ 😃 😐 😫 😴

➡ ➡ ➡ ➡ ➡ ➡ ➡ ➡ ➡ ➡ ➡ ➡ ➡ ➡

Total distance traveled: ___ KMs ☐ Miles ☐ Inches ☐

Walked ☐ Cycled ☐ Taxi ☐ Bus ☐ Plane ☐ Horse ☐
Other ☐ _____

➡ ➡ ➡ ➡ ➡ ➡ ➡ ➡ ➡ ➡ ➡ ➡ ➡ ➡

Stayed @: _____

Albergue ☐ Hostel ☐ Hotel ☐ Tent ☐ Under the stars ☐

➡ ➡ ➡ ➡ ➡ ➡ ➡ ➡ ➡ ➡ ➡ ➡ ➡

Ate: Breakfast ☐ _____

          Eat it again! ☐ So So ☐ Bleck ☐

       Lunch ☐ _____

          Eat it again! ☐ So So ☐ Bleck ☐

      Dinner ☐ _____

          Eat it again! ☐ So So ☐ Bleck ☐

Spent: _____ Euros ☐ Dollars ☐ Other ☐
On lodgings ☐ On food ☐ On Gifts ☐ Other ☐

➡ ➡ ➡ ➡ ➡ ➡ ➡ ➡ ➡ ➡ ➡ ➡ ➡ ➡

Tomorrow is a new day. Important things to remember:

_____

_____

_____

What is my purpose today? ♡

_____
_____
_____

Who am I to help? 🤝 With what?

_____
_____
_____

Who will help me? 🤝 With what?

_____
_____
_____

Lessons learned along The Way
Gifts from the Universe/GOD/Angels/Spirits

**1** _____

**2** _____

**3** _____

What piece of equipment am I most grateful for today?

_____

Angels (Pilgrims) I met on the Camino today:

Name: _____

Contact info: _____

Name: _____

Contact info: _____

# DAY 6 - MY THOUGHTS

As you start to walk out on the way, the way appears.
- Rumi -

_____

_____

_____

_____

_____

_____

_____

_____

_____

_____

_____

## DAY 6 - MINDFULNESS MINUTE

Body Check: Mark these feet with an X where you currently have or had blisters.

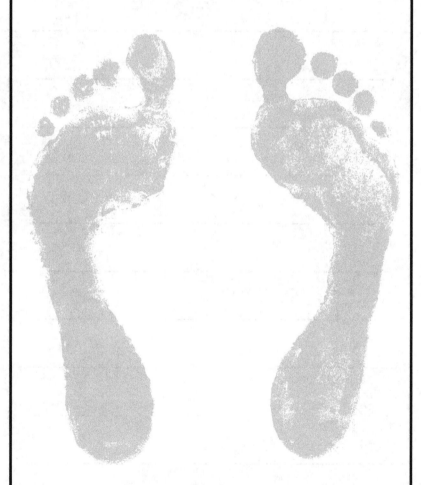

DO NOT pass GO!
Go directly and buy some Compede.

I found it helpful to individually wrap every other one of my toes with moleskin every morning.

# DAY 7

# DAY 7 - MY CAMINO

From: _____ to: _____

The weather is:                I am feeling:

☼  ☁  ☁  🌧  🌨        ☺  😄  😐  😖  😴

➡ ➡ ➡ ➡ ➡ ➡ ➡ ➡ ➡ ➡ ➡ ➡ ➡ ➡

Total distance traveled: ___ KMs ☐ Miles ☐ Inches ☐

Walked ☐ Cycled ☐ Taxi ☐ Bus ☐ Plane ☐ Horse ☐
Other ☐ _____

➡ ➡ ➡ ➡ ➡ ➡ ➡ ➡ ➡ ➡ ➡ ➡ ➡ ➡

Stayed @: _____

Albergue ☐ Hostel ☐ Hotel ☐ Tent ☐ Under the stars ☐

➡ ➡ ➡ ➡ ➡ ➡ ➡ ➡ ➡ ➡ ➡ ➡ ➡ ➡

Ate: Breakfast ☐ _____

        Eat it again! ☐  So So ☐  Bleck ☐

      Lunch ☐ _____

        Eat it again! ☐  So So ☐  Bleck ☐

     Dinner ☐ _____

        Eat it again! ☐  So So ☐  Bleck ☐

Spent: _____ Euros ☐  Dollars ☐  Other ☐
On lodgings ☐  On food ☐  On Gifts ☐  Other ☐

➡ ➡ ➡ ➡ ➡ ➡ ➡ ➡ ➡ ➡ ➡ ➡ ➡ ➡

Tomorrow is a new day. Important things to remember:

_____

_____

_____

# DAY 7 - MY PURPOSE

What is my purpose today? ♡

_____

_____

_____

Who am I to help? 🤝 With what?

_____

_____

_____

Who will help me? 🤝 With what?

_____

_____

_____

Lessons learned along The Way
Gifts from the Universe/GOD/Angels/Spirits

**1** _____

**2** _____

**3** _____

What piece of equipment am I most grateful for today?

_____

Angels (Pilgrims) I met on the Camino today:

Name: _____

Contact info: _____

Name: _____

Contact info: _____

Somewhere between the start of the trail and the end is the mystery why we choose to walk.
- Travelher.org -

_____

_____

_____

_____

_____

_____

_____

_____

_____

_____

# DAY 7 - MINDFULNESS MINUTE

Art Project: Doodle all over this page or draw the faces of the last three people you met and write what country they are from.

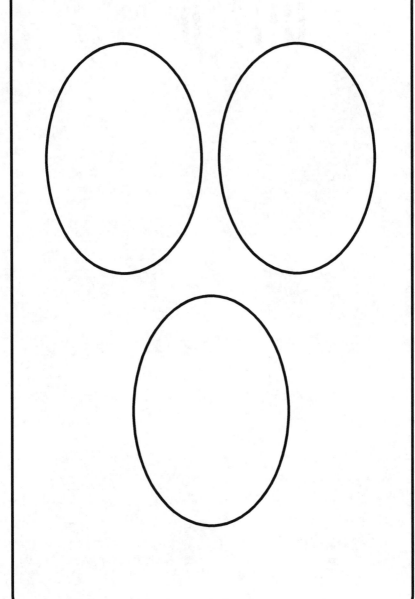

# DAY 8

# DAY 8 - MY CAMINO

From: _____ to: _____

The weather is:                    I am feeling:

☀ ☁ ⛅ 🌧 🌨          😊 😃 😑 😣 😴

➡ ➡ ➡ ➡ ➡ ➡ ➡ ➡ ➡ ➡ ➡ ➡ ➡

Total distance traveled: ____ KMs ☐ Miles ☐ Inches ☐

Walked ☐ Cycled ☐ Taxi ☐ Bus ☐ Plane ☐ Horse ☐
Other ☐ _____

➡ ➡ ➡ ➡ ➡ ➡ ➡ ➡ ➡ ➡ ➡ ➡ ➡

Stayed @: _____

Albergue ☐ Hostel ☐ Hotel ☐ Tent ☐ Under the stars ☐

➡ ➡ ➡ ➡ ➡ ➡ ➡ ➡ ➡ ➡ ➡ ➡ ➡

Ate: Breakfast ☐ _____

　　　　　　　Eat it again! ☐ So So ☐ Bleck ☐
　　　　Lunch ☐ _____

　　　　　　　Eat it again! ☐ So So ☐ Bleck ☐
　　　Dinner ☐ _____

　　　　　　　Eat it again! ☐ So So ☐ Bleck ☐

Spent: _____ Euros ☐ Dollars ☐ Other ☐
On lodgings ☐ On food ☐ On Gifts ☐ Other ☐

➡ ➡ ➡ ➡ ➡ ➡ ➡ ➡ ➡ ➡ ➡ ➡ ➡

Tomorrow is a new day. Important things to remember:

_____

_____

_____

## DAY 8 - MY PURPOSE

What is my purpose today? ♡

_____

_____

_____

Who am I to help? 🤝 With what?

_____

_____

_____

Who will help me? 🤝 With what?

_____

_____

_____

Lessons learned along The Way
Gifts from the Universe/GOD/Angels/Spirits

**1** _____

**2** _____

**3** _____

What piece of equipment am I most grateful for today?

_____

Angels (Pilgrims) I met on the Camino today:

Name: _____

Contact info: _____

Name: _____

Contact info: _____

# DAY 8 - MY THOUGHTS

The true miracle is not walking on water or walking on
air, but simply walking on this earth.
- Thich Nhat Hanh -

_____

_____

_____

_____

_____

_____

_____

_____

_____

_____

# DAY 8 - MINDFULNESS MINUTE

Act Like a Kid: Rub your wet boot in the beautiful red
Spanish earth and STOMP it here.

_____

_____

_____

_____

_____

_____

_____

_____

_____

_____

Bare feet or hands work too.

# DAY 9

# DAY 9 - MY CAMINO

From: _____ to: _____

The weather is:                    I am feeling:

☼   ☁   ⛅   🌧   ❄          ☺   😀   😐   😞   😴

➡ ➡ ➡ ➡ ➡ ➡ ➡ ➡ ➡ ➡ ➡ ➡ ➡

Total distance traveled: ____ KMs ☐ Miles ☐ Inches ☐

Walked ☐ Cycled ☐ Taxi ☐ Bus ☐ Plane ☐ Horse ☐
Other ☐ _____

➡ ➡ ➡ ➡ ➡ ➡ ➡ ➡ ➡ ➡ ➡ ➡ ➡

Stayed @: _____

Albergue ☐ Hostel ☐ Hotel ☐ Tent ☐ Under the stars ☐

➡ ➡ ➡ ➡ ➡ ➡ ➡ ➡ ➡ ➡ ➡ ➡ ➡

Ate: Breakfast ☐ _____

            Eat it again! ☐ So So ☐ Bleck ☐

      Lunch ☐ _____

            Eat it again! ☐ So So ☐ Bleck ☐

      Dinner ☐ _____

            Eat it again! ☐ So So ☐ Bleck ☐

Spent: _____ Euros ☐ Dollars ☐ Other ☐
On lodgings ☐ On food ☐ On Gifts ☐ Other ☐

➡ ➡ ➡ ➡ ➡ ➡ ➡ ➡ ➡ ➡ ➡ ➡ ➡

Tomorrow is a new day. Important things to remember:

_____

_____

_____

# DAY 9 - MY PURPOSE

What is my purpose today? ♡

_____
_____
_____

Who am I to help? 🤝 With what?

_____
_____
_____

Who will help me? 🤝 With what?

_____
_____
_____

Lessons learned along The Way
Gifts from the Universe/GOD/Angels/Spirits

**1** _____

**2** _____

**3** _____

What piece of equipment am I most grateful for today?

_____

Angels (Pilgrims) I met on the Camino today:

Name: _____

Contact info: _____

Name: _____

Contact info: _____

When you walk on the face of a world, then forgiveness comes.

- Orson Scott Card -

_____

_____

_____

_____

_____

_____

_____

_____

_____

_____

## DAY 9 - MINDFULNESS MINUTE

Reflect and Go Deep: While you walk today, begin to think of the people in your life that YOU need to forgive, and why.

List them here:

_____

_____

_____

_____

_____

_____

_____

_____

_____

_____

# DAY 10

# DAY 10 - MY CAMINO

From: _____ to: _____

The weather is:                    I am feeling:

☀ ☁ ⛅ 🌧 🌨          ☺ 😀 😑 😞 😴

➡ ➡ ➡ ➡ ➡ ➡ ➡ ➡ ➡ ➡ ➡ ➡ ➡ ➡

Total distance traveled: ___ KMs ☐ Miles ☐ Inches ☐
  Walked ☐ Cycled ☐ Taxi ☐ Bus ☐ Plane ☐ Horse ☐
  Other ☐ _____

➡ ➡ ➡ ➡ ➡ ➡ ➡ ➡ ➡ ➡ ➡ ➡ ➡ ➡

Stayed @: _____
Albergue ☐ Hostel ☐ Hotel ☐ Tent ☐ Under the stars ☐

➡ ➡ ➡ ➡ ➡ ➡ ➡ ➡ ➡ ➡ ➡ ➡ ➡ ➡

Ate: Breakfast ☐ _____
              Eat it again! ☐ So So ☐ Bleck ☐
        Lunch ☐ _____
              Eat it again! ☐ So So ☐ Bleck ☐
       Dinner ☐ _____
              Eat it again! ☐ So So ☐ Bleck ☐

Spent: _____ Euros ☐    Dollars ☐   Other ☐
On lodgings ☐  On food ☐  On Gifts ☐  Other ☐

➡ ➡ ➡ ➡ ➡ ➡ ➡ ➡ ➡ ➡ ➡ ➡ ➡ ➡

Tomorrow is a new day. Important things to remember:

_____
_____
_____

What is my purpose today? ♡

_____

_____

_____

Who am I to help? 🤝 With what?

_____

_____

_____

Who will help me? 🤝 With what?

_____

_____

_____

Lessons learned along The Way
Gifts from the Universe/GOD/Angels/Spirits

**1** _____

**2** _____

**3** _____

What piece of equipment am I most grateful for today?

_____

Angels (Pilgrims) I met on the Camino today:

Name: _____

Contact info: _____

Name: _____

Contact info: _____

# DAY 10 - MY THOUGHTS

We live within borrowed time and walk in rented shoes.
If we fade we fade, but let us go out having loved,
laughed and forgiven.

- Writtenbyhim -

_____

_____

_____

_____

_____

_____

_____

_____

_____

_____

# DAY 10 - MINDFULNESS MINUTE

BEST Camino story EVER! Yours or someone else's.

_____

_____

_____

_____

_____

What makes it better than all the others?

_____

_____

_____

_____

_____

_____

_____

# DAY 11

From: _____ to: _____

The weather is:                    I am feeling:

➡ ➡ ➡ ➡ ➡ ➡ ➡ ➡ ➡ ➡ ➡ ➡

Total distance traveled: ___ KMs ☐ Miles ☐ Inches ☐

Walked ☐ Cycled ☐ Taxi ☐ Bus ☐ Plane ☐ Horse ☐
Other ☐ _____

➡ ➡ ➡ ➡ ➡ ➡ ➡ ➡ ➡ ➡ ➡ ➡

Stayed @: _____

Albergue ☐ Hostel ☐ Hotel ☐ Tent ☐ Under the stars ☐

➡ ➡ ➡ ➡ ➡ ➡ ➡ ➡ ➡ ➡ ➡ ➡

Ate: Breakfast ☐ _____

Eat it again! ☐ So So ☐ Bleck ☐

Lunch ☐ _____

Eat it again! ☐ So So ☐ Bleck ☐

Dinner ☐ _____

Eat it again! ☐ So So ☐ Bleck ☐

Spent: _____ Euros ☐ Dollars ☐ Other ☐
On lodgings ☐ On food ☐ On Gifts ☐ Other ☐

➡ ➡ ➡ ➡ ➡ ➡ ➡ ➡ ➡ ➡ ➡ ➡

Tomorrow is a new day. Important things to remember:

_____

_____

_____

# DAY 11 - MY PURPOSE

What is my purpose today? ♡

_____
_____
_____

Who am I to help? 🤝 With what?

_____
_____
_____

Who will help me? 🤝 With what?

_____
_____
_____

Lessons learned along The Way
Gifts from the Universe/GOD/Angels/Spirits

**1** _____

**2** _____

**3** _____

What piece of equipment am I most grateful for today?

_____

Angels (Pilgrims) I met on the Camino today:

Name: _____

Contact info: _____

Name: _____

Contact info: _____

# DAY 11 - MY THOUGHTS

Do not judge my story by the chapter you walked in on.
- Unknown -

_____

_____

_____

_____

_____

_____

_____

_____

_____

_____

_____

_____

# DAY 11 - MINDFULNESS MINUTE

Honesty Matters: List the people or things you are
walking away from.

Write about the reasons why.

_____

_____

_____

_____

_____

_____

_____

_____

_____

_____

_____

_____

# DAY 12

# DAY 12 - MY CAMINO

From: _____ to: _____

The weather is:                I am feeling:

☀ ☁ ⛅ 🌧 🌨          ☺ 😃 😐 😞 😴

➡ ➡ ➡ ➡ ➡ ➡ ➡ ➡ ➡ ➡ ➡ ➡ ➡

Total distance traveled: ___ KMs ☐ Miles ☐ Inches ☐

   Walked ☐ Cycled ☐ Taxi ☐ Bus ☐ Plane ☐ Horse ☐
   Other ☐ _____

➡ ➡ ➡ ➡ ➡ ➡ ➡ ➡ ➡ ➡ ➡ ➡ ➡

Stayed @: _____

Albergue ☐ Hostel ☐ Hotel ☐ Tent ☐ Under the stars ☐

➡ ➡ ➡ ➡ ➡ ➡ ➡ ➡ ➡ ➡ ➡ ➡ ➡

Ate:  Breakfast ☐ _____

              Eat it again! ☐  So So ☐  Bleck ☐
         Lunch ☐ _____

              Eat it again! ☐  So So ☐  Bleck ☐
        Dinner ☐ _____

              Eat it again! ☐  So So ☐  Bleck ☐

Spent: _____ Euros ☐    Dollars ☐  Other ☐
On lodgings ☐  On food ☐  On Gifts ☐  Other ☐

➡ ➡ ➡ ➡ ➡ ➡ ➡ ➡ ➡ ➡ ➡ ➡ ➡

Tomorrow is a new day. Important things to remember:

_____

_____

_____

# DAY 12 - MY PURPOSE

What is my purpose today? ♡

_____
_____
_____

Who am I to help? 🤝 With what?

_____
_____
_____

Who will help me? 🤝 With what?

_____
_____
_____

Lessons learned along The Way
Gifts from the Universe/GOD/Angels/Spirits

**1** _____

**2** _____

**3** _____

What piece of equipment am I most grateful for today?

_____

Angels (Pilgrims) I met on the Camino today:

Name: _____

Contact info: _____

Name: _____

Contact info: _____

# DAY 12 - MY THOUGHTS

Shave it off and start all over again.
- KLM -

_____

_____

_____

_____

_____

_____

_____

_____

_____

_____

_____

# DAY 12 - MINDFULNESS MINUTE

Gratitude: List all of the things in your life that you are grateful for. Try to fill up the whole page. Write messy or use your non-dominant hand for fun.

_____

_____

_____

_____

_____

_____

_____

_____

_____

_____

_____

_____

# DAY 13

From: _____ to: _____

The weather is:                I am feeling:

☼  ☁  ⛅  🌧  🌨        ☺  😃  😐  😞  😴

➡ ➡ ➡ ➡ ➡ ➡ ➡ ➡ ➡ ➡ ➡ ➡

Total distance traveled: ____ KMs ☐ Miles ☐ Inches ☐

Walked ☐ Cycled ☐ Taxi ☐ Bus ☐ Plane ☐ Horse ☐
Other ☐ _____

➡ ➡ ➡ ➡ ➡ ➡ ➡ ➡ ➡ ➡ ➡ ➡

Stayed @: _____

Albergue ☐ Hostel ☐ Hotel ☐ Tent ☐ Under the stars ☐

➡ ➡ ➡ ➡ ➡ ➡ ➡ ➡ ➡ ➡ ➡ ➡

Ate: Breakfast ☐ _____

                Eat it again! ☐  So So ☐  Bleck ☐

          Lunch ☐ _____

                Eat it again! ☐  So So ☐  Bleck ☐

         Dinner ☐ _____

                Eat it again! ☐  So So ☐  Bleck ☐

Spent: _____ Euros ☐  Dollars ☐  Other ☐
On lodgings ☐  On food ☐  On Gifts ☐  Other ☐

➡ ➡ ➡ ➡ ➡ ➡ ➡ ➡ ➡ ➡ ➡ ➡

Tomorrow is a new day. Important things to remember:

_____

_____

_____

# DAY 13 - MY PURPOSE

What is my purpose today? ♡

_____

_____

_____

Who am I to help? 🤝 With what?

_____

_____

_____

Who will help me? 🤝 With what?

_____

_____

_____

Lessons learned along The Way
Gifts from the Universe/GOD/Angels/Spirits

**1** _____

**2** _____

**3** _____

What piece of equipment am I most grateful for today?

_____

Angels (Pilgrims) I met on the Camino today:

Name: _____

Contact info: _____

Name: _____

Contact info: _____

My grandmother started walking 5 miles a day when she was 60. She is 97 today and we don't know where the hell she is.

- Ellen DeGeneres -

_____

_____

_____

_____

_____

_____

_____

_____

_____

_____

## DAY 13 - MINDFULNESS MINUTE

Clear the Clutter: What are some of the items from
your backpack that you have chosen to leave behind?
Come back to this page at the end and finish the list.

_____

_____

_____

_____

_____

_____

_____

_____

_____

_____

_____

# DAY 14

# DAY 14 - MY CAMINO

From: _____ to: _____

The weather is:                    I am feeling:

☀ ☁ ⛅ 🌧 🌨                😊 😄 😐 😣 😴

➡ ➡ ➡ ➡ ➡ ➡ ➡ ➡ ➡ ➡ ➡ ➡ ➡

Total distance traveled: ___ KMs ☐ Miles ☐ Inches ☐

Walked ☐ Cycled ☐ Taxi ☐ Bus ☐ Plane ☐ Horse ☐
Other ☐ _____

➡ ➡ ➡ ➡ ➡ ➡ ➡ ➡ ➡ ➡ ➡ ➡ ➡

Stayed @: _____

Albergue ☐ Hostel ☐ Hotel ☐ Tent ☐ Under the stars ☐

➡ ➡ ➡ ➡ ➡ ➡ ➡ ➡ ➡ ➡ ➡ ➡ ➡

Ate: Breakfast ☐ _____

                Eat it again! ☐  So So ☐  Bleck ☐

        Lunch ☐ _____

                Eat it again! ☐  So So ☐  Bleck ☐

        Dinner ☐ _____

                Eat it again! ☐  So So ☐  Bleck ☐

Spent: _____ Euros ☐    Dollars ☐   Other ☐
On lodgings ☐ On food ☐  On Gifts ☐  Other ☐

➡ ➡ ➡ ➡ ➡ ➡ ➡ ➡ ➡ ➡ ➡ ➡ ➡

Tomorrow is a new day. Important things to remember:

_____

_____

_____

# DAY 14 - MY PURPOSE

What is my purpose today? ♡

_____
_____
_____

Who am I to help? 🤝 With what?

_____
_____
_____

Who will help me? 🤝 With what?

_____
_____
_____

Lessons learned along The Way
Gifts from the Universe/GOD/Angels/Spirits

**1** _____

**2** _____

**3** _____

What piece of equipment am I most grateful for today?

_____

Angels (Pilgrims) I met on the Camino today:

Name: _____

Contact info: _____

Name: _____

Contact info: _____

## DAY 14 - MY THOUGHTS

All truly great thoughts are conceived by walking.
- Fredrich Nietzsche -

_____

_____

_____

_____

_____

_____

_____

_____

_____

_____

_____

_____

# DAY 14 - MINDFULNESS MINUTE

Time to send a letter or some postcards.
List the lucky recipients here:

_____

_____

_____

_____

_____

_____

_____

_____

_____

Why not write the addresses here before
you leave home so you have them in
one place when you need them.

# DAY 15

From: _____ to: _____

The weather is:                I am feeling:

☀ ☁ ⛅ 🌧 🌨        ☺ 😀 😐 😣 😴

➡ ➡ ➡ ➡ ➡ ➡ ➡ ➡ ➡ ➡ ➡ ➡ ➡

Total distance traveled: ____ KMs ☐ Miles ☐ Inches ☐

Walked ☐ Cycled ☐ Taxi ☐ Bus ☐ Plane ☐ Horse ☐
Other ☐ _____

➡ ➡ ➡ ➡ ➡ ➡ ➡ ➡ ➡ ➡ ➡ ➡ ➡

Stayed @: _____

Albergue ☐ Hostel ☐ Hotel ☐ Tent ☐ Under the stars ☐

➡ ➡ ➡ ➡ ➡ ➡ ➡ ➡ ➡ ➡ ➡ ➡ ➡

Ate: Breakfast ☐ _____

Eat it again! ☐ So So ☐ Bleck ☐

Lunch ☐ _____

Eat it again! ☐ So So ☐ Bleck ☐

Dinner ☐ _____

Eat it again! ☐ So So ☐ Bleck ☐

Spent: _____ Euros ☐ Dollars ☐ Other ☐
On lodgings ☐ On food ☐ On Gifts ☐ Other ☐

➡ ➡ ➡ ➡ ➡ ➡ ➡ ➡ ➡ ➡ ➡ ➡ ➡

Tomorrow is a new day. Important things to remember:

_____

_____

_____

# DAY 15 - MY PURPOSE

What is my purpose today? ♡

_____

_____

_____

Who am I to help? 🤝 With what?

_____

_____

_____

Who will help me? 🤝 With what?

_____

_____

_____

Lessons learned along The Way
Gifts from the Universe/GOD/Angels/Spirits

**1** _____

**2** _____

**3** _____

What piece of equipment am I most grateful for today?

_____

Angels (Pilgrims) I met on the Camino today:

Name: _____

Contact info: _____

Name: _____

Contact info: _____

I am not walking by sight—I am walking by faith.
- T.D. Jakes -

_____

_____

_____

_____

_____

_____

_____

_____

_____

_____

_____

# DAY 15 - MINDFULNESS MINUTE

Hardship Meter: What has been your most difficult day?
List the reasons why below:

_____

_____

_____

_____

_____

_____

_____

_____

_____

_____

_____

Have you taken any wrong turns?

# DAY 16

# DAY 16 - MY CAMINO

From: _____ to: _____

The weather is:                    I am feeling:

☀ ☁ ⛅ 🌧 🌨                    ☺ ☺ 😐 😞 😴

➡ ➡ ➡ ➡ ➡ ➡ ➡ ➡ ➡ ➡ ➡ ➡ ➡

Total distance traveled: ___ KMs ☐ Miles ☐ Inches ☐

  Walked ☐ Cycled ☐ Taxi ☐ Bus ☐ Plane ☐ Horse ☐
  Other ☐ _____

➡ ➡ ➡ ➡ ➡ ➡ ➡ ➡ ➡ ➡ ➡ ➡ ➡

Stayed @: _____

Albergue ☐ Hostel ☐ Hotel ☐ Tent ☐ Under the stars ☐

➡ ➡ ➡ ➡ ➡ ➡ ➡ ➡ ➡ ➡ ➡ ➡ ➡

Ate:  Breakfast ☐ _____

              Eat it again! ☐  So So ☐  Bleck ☐
       Lunch ☐ _____

              Eat it again! ☐  So So ☐  Bleck ☐
      Dinner ☐ _____

              Eat it again! ☐  So So ☐  Bleck ☐

Spent: _____ Euros ☐  Dollars ☐  Other ☐
On lodgings ☐  On food ☐  On Gifts ☐  Other ☐

➡ ➡ ➡ ➡ ➡ ➡ ➡ ➡ ➡ ➡ ➡ ➡ ➡

Tomorrow is a new day. Important things to remember:

_____

_____

_____

What is my purpose today? ♡

_____
_____
_____

Who am I to help? 🤝 With what?

_____
_____
_____

Who will help me? 🤝 With what?

_____
_____
_____

Lessons learned along The Way
Gifts from the Universe/GOD/Angels/Spirits

**1** _____

**2** _____

**3** _____

What piece of equipment am I most grateful for today?

_____

Angels (Pilgrims) I met on the Camino today:

Name: _____

Contact info: _____

Name: _____

Contact info: _____

# DAY 16 - MY THOUGHTS

If we are facing in the right direction, all we have to
do is keep on walking.
                              - Zen Proverbs -

_____

_____

_____

_____

_____

_____

_____

_____

_____

_____

# DAY 16 - MINDFULNESS MINUTE

Hardship Meter: What has been your easiest day so far?
List the reasons why below:

_____

_____

_____

_____

_____

_____

_____

_____

_____

_____

What were some of the things or people that
contributed to the day running smoothly?

# DAY 17

# DAY 17 - MY CAMINO

From: _____ to: _____

The weather is:                    I am feeling:

☀ ☁ ⛅ 🌧 🌨        ☺ 😀 😐 😖 😴

➡ ➡ ➡ ➡ ➡ ➡ ➡ ➡ ➡ ➡ ➡ ➡ ➡ ➡

Total distance traveled: ___ KMs ☐ Miles ☐ Inches ☐

Walked ☐ Cycled ☐ Taxi ☐ Bus ☐ Plane ☐ Horse ☐
Other ☐ _____

➡ ➡ ➡ ➡ ➡ ➡ ➡ ➡ ➡ ➡ ➡ ➡ ➡ ➡

Stayed @: _____

Albergue ☐ Hostel ☐ Hotel ☐ Tent ☐ Under the stars ☐

➡ ➡ ➡ ➡ ➡ ➡ ➡ ➡ ➡ ➡ ➡ ➡ ➡ ➡

Ate:  Breakfast ☐ _____

               Eat it again! ☐ So So ☐ Bleck ☐
         Lunch ☐ _____

               Eat it again! ☐ So So ☐ Bleck ☐
        Dinner ☐ _____

               Eat it again! ☐ So So ☐ Bleck ☐

Spent: _____ Euros ☐  Dollars ☐ Other ☐
On lodgings ☐ On food ☐ On Gifts ☐ Other ☐

➡ ➡ ➡ ➡ ➡ ➡ ➡ ➡ ➡ ➡ ➡ ➡ ➡ ➡

Tomorrow is a new day. Important things to remember:

_____

_____

_____

# DAY 17 - MY PURPOSE

What is my purpose today? ♡

_____
_____
_____

Who am I to help? 🤝 With what?

_____
_____
_____

Who will help me? 🤝 With what?

_____
_____
_____

Lessons learned along The Way
Gifts from the Universe/GOD/Angels/Spirits

**1** _____

**2** _____

**3** _____

What piece of equipment am I most grateful for today?

_____

Angels (Pilgrims) I met on the Camino today:

Name: _____

Contact info: _____

Name: _____

Contact info: _____

Good things are coming down the road. Just don't stop walking.

- Robert Warren Painter, Jr. -

_____

_____

_____

_____

_____

_____

_____

_____

_____

_____

_____

## DAY 17 - MINDFULNESS MINUTE

Un-Favorite...
Place to stay: _____

Meal: _____

Angel (Pilgrim): _____

_____

Moment: _____

_____

Favorite...
Place to stay: _____

Meal: _____

Angel (Pilgrim): _____

_____

Moment: _____

_____

View: _____

_____

Monument/Architecture: _____

_____

I hope your list of favorites is longer.

# DAY 18

# DAY 18 - MY CAMINO

From: _____ to: _____

The weather is:       I am feeling:

☀ ☁ ⛅ 🌧 🌨       ☺ 😃 😐 😣 😴

➡ ➡ ➡ ➡ ➡ ➡ ➡ ➡ ➡ ➡ ➡ ➡ ➡

Total distance traveled: ___ KMs ☐ Miles ☐ Inches ☐

Walked ☐ Cycled ☐ Taxi ☐ Bus ☐ Plane ☐ Horse ☐
Other ☐ _____

➡ ➡ ➡ ➡ ➡ ➡ ➡ ➡ ➡ ➡ ➡ ➡ ➡

Stayed @: _____

Albergue ☐ Hostel ☐ Hotel ☐ Tent ☐ Under the stars ☐

➡ ➡ ➡ ➡ ➡ ➡ ➡ ➡ ➡ ➡ ➡ ➡ ➡

Ate: Breakfast ☐ _____

         Eat it again! ☐ So So ☐ Bleck ☐

     Lunch ☐ _____

         Eat it again! ☐ So So ☐ Bleck ☐

    Dinner ☐ _____

         Eat it again! ☐ So So ☐ Bleck ☐

Spent: _____ Euros ☐ Dollars ☐ Other ☐
On lodgings ☐ On food ☐ On Gifts ☐ Other ☐

➡ ➡ ➡ ➡ ➡ ➡ ➡ ➡ ➡ ➡ ➡ ➡ ➡

Tomorrow is a new day. Important things to remember:

_____

_____

_____

## DAY 18 - MY PURPOSE

What is my purpose today? ♡

_____
_____
_____

Who am I to help? 🤝 With what?

_____
_____
_____

Who will help me? 💜 With what?

_____
_____
_____

Lessons learned along The Way
Gifts from the Universe/GOD/Angels/Spirits

**1** _____

**2** _____

**3** _____

What piece of equipment am I most grateful for today?

_____

Angels (Pilgrims) I met on the Camino today:

Name: _____

Contact info: _____

Name: _____

Contact info: _____

# DAY 18 - MY THOUGHTS

Walking is the best possible exercise. Habituate yourself
to walk very far.

- Thomas Jefferson -

_____

_____

_____

_____

_____

_____

_____

_____

_____

_____

# DAY 18 - MINDFULNESS MINUTE

Tell Your Story: If the Cruze de Ferro is on your itinerary, take a picture of the stones you plan to lay at the bottom of the cross. Did you visit another sacred place instead?

Place the picture here. Write about your stones.

Did you leave any other
special mementos along the way?

# DAY 19

From: _____ to: _____

The weather is:                I am feeling:

☀ ☁ ☁ 🌧 🌨            ☺ 😃 😐 😖 😴

➡ ➡ ➡ ➡ ➡ ➡ ➡ ➡ ➡ ➡ ➡ ➡ ➡

Total distance traveled: ___ KMs ☐ Miles ☐ Inches ☐

Walked ☐ Cycled ☐ Taxi ☐ Bus ☐ Plane ☐ Horse ☐
Other ☐ _____

➡ ➡ ➡ ➡ ➡ ➡ ➡ ➡ ➡ ➡ ➡ ➡ ➡

Stayed @: _____

Albergue ☐ Hostel ☐ Hotel ☐ Tent ☐ Under the stars ☐

➡ ➡ ➡ ➡ ➡ ➡ ➡ ➡ ➡ ➡ ➡ ➡ ➡

Ate: Breakfast ☐ _____

Eat it again! ☐  So So ☐  Bleck ☐

Lunch ☐ _____

Eat it again! ☐  So So ☐  Bleck ☐

Dinner ☐ _____

Eat it again! ☐  So So ☐  Bleck ☐

Spent: _____ Euros ☐  Dollars ☐  Other ☐
On lodgings ☐  On food ☐  On Gifts ☐  Other ☐

➡ ➡ ➡ ➡ ➡ ➡ ➡ ➡ ➡ ➡ ➡ ➡ ➡

Tomorrow is a new day. Important things to remember:

_____

_____

_____

# DAY 19 - MY PURPOSE

What is my purpose today? ♡

_____
_____
_____

Who am I to help? 🤝 With what?

_____
_____
_____

Who will help me? 🤝 With what?

_____
_____
_____

Lessons learned along The Way
Gifts from the Universe/GOD/Angels/Spirits

**1** _____

**2** _____

**3** _____

What piece of equipment am I most grateful for today?

_____

Angels (Pilgrims) I met on the Camino today:

Name: _____

Contact info: _____

Name: _____

Contact info: _____

# DAY 19 - MY THOUGHTS

If you are seeking creative ideas go out walking. Angels whisper to a man when he goes for a walk.
- Raymond Inmon -

_____

_____

_____

_____

_____

_____

_____

_____

_____

_____

_____

## DAY 19 - MINDFULNESS MINUTE

Tune In: How does music heal your weary soul? Did you bring music with you or have you chosen to walk in silence?

_____

_____

_____

_____

_____

_____

_____

_____

_____

What songs or lyrics have gotten you through
the toughest times in your life?

# DAY 20

# DAY 20 - MY CAMINO

From: _____ to: _____

The weather is:　　　　I am feeling:

☼　☁　⛅　🌧　❄️　　☺️　😀　😐　😟　😴

➡️ ➡️ ➡️ ➡️ ➡️ ➡️ ➡️ ➡️ ➡️ ➡️ ➡️ ➡️ ➡️

Total distance traveled: ___ KMs ☐ Miles ☐ Inches ☐

Walked ☐ Cycled ☐ Taxi ☐ Bus ☐ Plane ☐ Horse ☐
Other ☐ _____

➡️ ➡️ ➡️ ➡️ ➡️ ➡️ ➡️ ➡️ ➡️ ➡️ ➡️ ➡️ ➡️

Stayed @: _____
Albergue ☐ Hostel ☐ Hotel ☐ Tent ☐ Under the stars ☐

➡️ ➡️ ➡️ ➡️ ➡️ ➡️ ➡️ ➡️ ➡️ ➡️ ➡️ ➡️ ➡️

Ate: Breakfast ☐ _____

　　　　　　Eat it again! ☐　So So ☐　Bleck ☐
　　　Lunch ☐ _____

　　　　　　Eat it again! ☐　So So ☐　Bleck ☐
　　　Dinner ☐ _____

　　　　　　Eat it again! ☐　So So ☐　Bleck ☐

Spent: _____ Euros ☐　Dollars ☐　Other ☐
On lodgings ☐　On food ☐　On Gifts ☐　Other ☐

➡️ ➡️ ➡️ ➡️ ➡️ ➡️ ➡️ ➡️ ➡️ ➡️ ➡️ ➡️ ➡️

Tomorrow is a new day. Important things to remember:

_____

_____

_____

# DAY 20 - MY PURPOSE

What is my purpose today? ♡

_____

_____

_____

Who am I to help? 🤝 With what?

_____

_____

_____

Who will help me? 🤝 With what?

_____

_____

_____

Lessons learned along The Way
Gifts from the Universe/GOD/Angels/Spirits

**1** _____

**2** _____

**3** _____

What piece of equipment am I most grateful for today?

_____

Angels (Pilgrims) I met on the Camino today:

Name: _____

Contact info: _____

Name: _____

Contact info: _____

# DAY 20 - MY THOUGHTS

Walking with a friend in the dark is better than walking
alone in the light.
                    - Helen Keller -

_____

_____

_____

_____

_____

_____

_____

_____

_____

_____

_____

# DAY 20 - MINDFULNESS MINUTE

Magical Mystery: Were there any days where you felt
that angels were carrying you?

_____

_____

_____

_____

_____

_____

_____

_____

_____

_____

Have the arrows been good to you?
Have they betrayed you?

# DAY 21

From: _____ to: _____

The weather is:                    I am feeling:

☀ ☁ ⛅ 🌧 ❄                    ☺ 😃 😐 😣 😴

➡➡➡➡➡➡➡➡➡➡➡➡➡➡➡

Total distance traveled: ___ KMs ☐ Miles ☐ Inches ☐

Walked ☐ Cycled ☐ Taxi ☐ Bus ☐ Plane ☐ Horse ☐
Other ☐ _____

➡➡➡➡➡➡➡➡➡➡➡➡➡➡➡

Stayed @: _____

Albergue ☐ Hostel ☐ Hotel ☐ Tent ☐ Under the stars ☐

➡➡➡➡➡➡➡➡➡➡➡➡➡➡➡

Ate: Breakfast ☐ _____

        Eat it again! ☐  So So ☐  Bleck ☐
    Lunch ☐ _____

        Eat it again! ☐  So So ☐  Bleck ☐
    Dinner ☐ _____

        Eat it again! ☐  So So ☐  Bleck ☐

Spent: _____ Euros ☐   Dollars ☐  Other ☐
On lodgings ☐  On food ☐  On Gifts ☐  Other ☐

➡➡➡➡➡➡➡➡➡➡➡➡➡➡➡

Tomorrow is a new day. Important things to remember:

_____
_____
_____

# DAY 21 - MY PURPOSE

What is my purpose today? ♡

_____

_____

_____

Who am I to help? 🤝 With what?

_____

_____

_____

Who will help me? 🤝 With what?

_____

_____

_____

Lessons learned along The Way
Gifts from the Universe/GOD/Angels/Spirits

**1** _____

**2** _____

**3** _____

What piece of equipment am I most grateful for today?

_____

Angels (Pilgrims) I met on the Camino today:

Name: _____

Contact info: _____

Name: _____

Contact info: _____

Some walks you have to take alone.
        - Suzanne Collins -

_____

_____

_____

_____

_____

_____

_____

_____

_____

_____

_____

_____

# DAY 21 - MINDFULNESS MINUTE

Spill the Beans: Has there been any place you have
visited on your journey that has unnerved or frightened
you?

_____

_____

_____

_____

_____

_____

_____

_____

_____

_____

_____

# DAY 22

# DAY 22 – MY CAMINO

From: _____ to: _____

The weather is:                    I am feeling:

☀ ☁ ⛅ 🌧 ❄               ☺ 😀 😐 😣 😴

➡ ➡ ➡ ➡ ➡ ➡ ➡ ➡ ➡ ➡ ➡ ➡ ➡

Total distance traveled: ___ KMs ☐ Miles ☐ Inches ☐

Walked ☐ Cycled ☐ Taxi ☐ Bus ☐ Plane ☐ Horse ☐
Other ☐ _____

➡ ➡ ➡ ➡ ➡ ➡ ➡ ➡ ➡ ➡ ➡ ➡ ➡

Stayed @: _____

Albergue ☐ Hostel ☐ Hotel ☐ Tent ☐ Under the stars ☐

➡ ➡ ➡ ➡ ➡ ➡ ➡ ➡ ➡ ➡ ➡ ➡ ➡

Ate:  Breakfast ☐ _____

Eat it again! ☐  So So ☐  Bleck ☐

Lunch ☐ _____

Eat it again! ☐  So So ☐  Bleck ☐

Dinner ☐ _____

Eat it again! ☐  So So ☐  Bleck ☐

Spent: _____ Euros ☐   Dollars ☐  Other ☐
On lodgings ☐  On food ☐  On Gifts ☐  Other ☐

➡ ➡ ➡ ➡ ➡ ➡ ➡ ➡ ➡ ➡ ➡ ➡ ➡

Tomorrow is a new day. Important things to remember:

_____
_____
_____

What is my purpose today? ♡

_____

_____

_____

Who am I to help? 🤝 With what?

_____

_____

_____

Who will help me? 🤝 With what?

_____

_____

_____

Lessons learned along The Way
Gifts from the Universe/GOD/Angels/Spirits

**1** _____

**2** _____

**3** _____

What piece of equipment am I most grateful for today?

_____

Angels (Pilgrims) I met on the Camino today:

Name: _____

Contact info: _____

Name: _____

Contact info: _____

# DAY 22 - MY THOUGHTS

There's a difference between knowing the path and walking the path.
- PictureQuotes.com -

_____

_____

_____

_____

_____

_____

_____

_____

_____

_____

_____

Snap Shot: Place your favorite Camino photo here. Write about why is it your favorite?

_____

_____

_____

# DAY 23

# DAY 23 - MY CAMINO

From: _____ to: _____

The weather is:                    I am feeling:

☼ ☁ ⛅ 🌧 ❄               ☺ 😃 😐 😣 😴

➡ ➡ ➡ ➡ ➡ ➡ ➡ ➡ ➡ ➡ ➡ ➡ ➡

Total distance traveled: ____ KMs ☐ Miles ☐ Inches ☐

Walked ☐ Cycled ☐ Taxi ☐ Bus ☐ Plane ☐ Horse ☐
Other ☐ _____

➡ ➡ ➡ ➡ ➡ ➡ ➡ ➡ ➡ ➡ ➡ ➡ ➡

Stayed @: _____

Albergue☐ Hostel☐ Hotel☐ Tent☐ Under the stars☐

➡ ➡ ➡ ➡ ➡ ➡ ➡ ➡ ➡ ➡ ➡ ➡ ➡

Ate: Breakfast ☐ _____

        Eat it again! ☐  So So ☐  Bleck ☐
        Lunch ☐ _____

        Eat it again! ☐  So So ☐  Bleck ☐
        Dinner ☐ _____

        Eat it again! ☐  So So ☐  Bleck ☐

Spent: _____ Euros ☐   Dollars ☐  Other ☐
On lodgings ☐  On food ☐  On Gifts ☐  Other ☐

➡ ➡ ➡ ➡ ➡ ➡ ➡ ➡ ➡ ➡ ➡ ➡ ➡

Tomorrow is a new day. Important things to remember:

_____

_____

_____

# DAY 23 - MY PURPOSE

What is my purpose today? ♡

_____

_____

_____

Who am I to help? 🤝 With what?

_____

_____

_____

Who will help me? 🤝 With what?

_____

_____

_____

Lessons learned along The Way
Gifts from the Universe/GOD/Angels/Spirits

**1** _____

**2** _____

**3** _____

What piece of equipment am I most grateful for today?

_____

Angels (Pilgrims) I met on the Camino today:

Name: _____

Contact info: _____

Name: _____

Contact info: _____

Success is walking from failure to failure with no loss
of enthusiasm
- Winston Churchill -

_____

_____

_____

_____

_____

_____

_____

_____

_____

_____

# DAY 23 - MINDFULNESS MINUTE

In the Know: John Kabat-Zinn writes that "compassion and kindness towards oneself are intrinsically woven into mindfulness."

Write a kindness promise to yourself.

_____

_____

_____

_____

_____

_____

_____

_____

_____

_____

That was easy, wasn't it?! You are worth it!

# DAY 24

# DAY 24 - MY CAMINO

From: _____ to: _____

The weather is:                    I am feeling:

☀ ☁ ⛅ 🌧 ❄            ☺ 😄 😐 😣 😴

➡ ➡ ➡ ➡ ➡ ➡ ➡ ➡ ➡ ➡ ➡ ➡ ➡ ➡

Total distance traveled: ___ KMs ☐ Miles ☐ Inches ☐

Walked ☐ Cycled ☐ Taxi ☐ Bus ☐ Plane ☐ Horse ☐
Other ☐ _____

➡ ➡ ➡ ➡ ➡ ➡ ➡ ➡ ➡ ➡ ➡ ➡ ➡ ➡

Stayed @: _____

Albergue ☐ Hostel ☐ Hotel ☐ Tent ☐ Under the stars ☐

➡ ➡ ➡ ➡ ➡ ➡ ➡ ➡ ➡ ➡ ➡ ➡ ➡

Ate: Breakfast ☐ _____

　　　　　　Eat it again! ☐ So So ☐ Bleck ☐

　　　Lunch ☐ _____

　　　　　　Eat it again! ☐ So So ☐ Bleck ☐

　　Dinner ☐ _____

　　　　　　Eat it again! ☐ So So ☐ Bleck ☐

Spent: _____ Euros ☐ Dollars ☐ Other ☐
On lodgings ☐ On food ☐ On Gifts ☐ Other ☐

➡ ➡ ➡ ➡ ➡ ➡ ➡ ➡ ➡ ➡ ➡ ➡ ➡ ➡

Tomorrow is a new day. Important things to remember:

_____

_____

_____

# DAY 24 - MY PURPOSE

What is my purpose today? ♡

_____

_____

_____

Who am I to help? 🤝 With what?

_____

_____

_____

Who will help me? 🤝 With what?

_____

_____

_____

Lessons learned along The Way
Gifts from the Universe/GOD/Angels/Spirits

**1** _____

**2** _____

**3** _____

What piece of equipment am I most grateful for today?

_____

Angels (Pilgrims) I met on the Camino today:

Name: _____

Contact info: _____

Name: _____

Contact info: _____

# DAY 24 - MY THOUGHTS

Walking is cheap, fun, safe and acceptable exercise.
- Annie Taylor -

_____

_____

_____

_____

_____

_____

_____

_____

_____

_____

_____

_____

# DAY 24 - MINDFULNESS MINUTE

Reflect and Go Deep: We ALL have things from our past that we need to let go of. What are some of the things you are willing to let go of…Today?

_____

_____

_____

_____

_____

_____

_____

_____

_____

_____

On a scale of 1-10, how easy was that?

# DAY 25

From: _____ to: _____

The weather is:                    I am feeling:

Total distance traveled: ____ KMs ☐ Miles ☐ Inches ☐
  Walked ☐ Cycled ☐ Taxi ☐ Bus ☐ Plane ☐ Horse ☐
  Other ☐ _____

Stayed @: _____
Albergue ☐ Hostel ☐ Hotel ☐ Tent ☐ Under the stars ☐

Ate: Breakfast ☐ _____
            Eat it again! ☐ So So ☐ Bleck ☐
        Lunch ☐ _____
            Eat it again! ☐ So So ☐ Bleck ☐
       Dinner ☐ _____
            Eat it again! ☐ So So ☐ Bleck ☐

Spent: _____ Euros ☐ Dollars ☐ Other ☐
On lodgings ☐ On food ☐ On Gifts ☐ Other ☐

Tomorrow is a new day. Important things to remember:

_____
_____
_____

# DAY 25 - MY PURPOSE

What is my purpose today? ♡

_____

_____

_____

Who am I to help? 🤝 With what?

_____

_____

_____

Who will help me? 💜 With what?

_____

_____

_____

Lessons learned along The Way
Gifts from the Universe/GOD/Angels/Spirits

**1** _____

**2** _____

**3** _____

What piece of equipment am I most grateful for today?

_____

Angels (Pilgrims) I met on the Camino today:

Name: _____

Contact info: _____

Name: _____

Contact info: _____

Happiness walks on busy feet.
- Kitte Turmell -

_____

_____

_____

_____

_____

_____

_____

_____

_____

_____

_____

# DAY 25 - MINDFULNESS MINUTE

Open Your Eyes: Slow down to the pace of a snail. List
eight things (or more) that you see clearly when you
look closely at the world in front of you.

_____

_____

_____

_____

_____

_____

_____

_____

_____

If you were still traveling at a faster pace,
would you have noticed them?

# DAY 26

# DAY 26 - MY CAMINO

From: _____ to: _____

The weather is:                    I am feeling:

☼  ☁  ⛅  🌧  🌨          ☺  😄  😐  😣  😴

➡ ➡ ➡ ➡ ➡ ➡ ➡ ➡ ➡ ➡ ➡ ➡ ➡ ➡

Total distance traveled: ___ KMs ☐ Miles ☐ Inches ☐

Walked ☐ Cycled ☐ Taxi ☐ Bus ☐ Plane ☐ Horse ☐
Other ☐ _____

➡ ➡ ➡ ➡ ➡ ➡ ➡ ➡ ➡ ➡ ➡ ➡ ➡ ➡

Stayed @: _____

Albergue ☐ Hostel ☐ Hotel ☐ Tent ☐ Under the stars ☐

➡ ➡ ➡ ➡ ➡ ➡ ➡ ➡ ➡ ➡ ➡ ➡ ➡

Ate:  Breakfast ☐ _____

          Eat it again! ☐  So So ☐  Bleck ☐

       Lunch ☐ _____

          Eat it again! ☐  So So ☐  Bleck ☐

       Dinner ☐ _____

          Eat it again! ☐  So So ☐  Bleck ☐

Spent: _____ Euros ☐  Dollars ☐  Other ☐
On lodgings ☐  On food ☐  On Gifts ☐  Other ☐

➡ ➡ ➡ ➡ ➡ ➡ ➡ ➡ ➡ ➡ ➡ ➡ ➡ ➡

Tomorrow is a new day. Important things to remember:

_____

_____

_____

What is my purpose today? ♡

_____
_____
_____

Who am I to help? 🤝 With what?

_____
_____
_____

Who will help me? 🤝 With what?

_____
_____
_____

Lessons learned along The Way
Gifts from the Universe/GOD/Angels/Spirits

**1** _____

**2** _____

**3** _____

What piece of equipment am I most grateful for today?

_____

Angels (Pilgrims) I met on the Camino today:

Name: _____

Contact info: _____

Name: _____

Contact info: _____

# DAY 26 - MY THOUGHTS

Don't look back, just keep on walking.
- Anonymous -

_____

_____

_____

_____

_____

_____

_____

_____

_____

_____

_____

_____

# DAY 26 - MINDFULNESS MINUTE

The Who's Who: Who are the people in your life who were the most supportive when you told them you were planning to walk the CAMINO?

_____

_____

_____

_____

_____

_____

_____

_____

_____

_____

Have they been following your journey?

# DAY 27

# DAY 27 - MY CAMINO

From: _____ to: _____

The weather is:                I am feeling:

☀ ☁ ⛅ 🌧 ❄          ☺ 😃 😐 😣 😴

➡ ➡ ➡ ➡ ➡ ➡ ➡ ➡ ➡ ➡ ➡ ➡ ➡

Total distance traveled: ___ KMs ☐ Miles ☐ Inches ☐

Walked ☐ Cycled ☐ Taxi ☐ Bus ☐ Plane ☐ Horse ☐
Other ☐ _____

➡ ➡ ➡ ➡ ➡ ➡ ➡ ➡ ➡ ➡ ➡ ➡ ➡

Stayed @: _____

Albergue ☐ Hostel ☐ Hotel ☐ Tent ☐ Under the stars ☐

➡ ➡ ➡ ➡ ➡ ➡ ➡ ➡ ➡ ➡ ➡ ➡ ➡

Ate: Breakfast ☐ _____

Eat it again! ☐ So So ☐ Bleck ☐

Lunch ☐ _____

Eat it again! ☐ So So ☐ Bleck ☐

Dinner ☐ _____

Eat it again! ☐ So So ☐ Bleck ☐

Spent: _____ Euros ☐ Dollars ☐ Other ☐
On lodgings ☐ On food ☐ On Gifts ☐ Other ☐

➡ ➡ ➡ ➡ ➡ ➡ ➡ ➡ ➡ ➡ ➡ ➡ ➡

Tomorrow is a new day. Important things to remember:

_____

_____

_____

# DAY 27 - MY PURPOSE

What is my purpose today? ♡

_____

_____

_____

Who am I to help? 🤝 With what?

_____

_____

_____

Who will help me? 🤝 With what?

_____

_____

_____

Lessons learned along The Way
Gifts from the Universe/GOD/Angels/Spirits

**1** _____

**2** _____

**3** _____

What piece of equipment am I most grateful for today?

_____

Angels (Pilgrims) I met on the Camino today:

Name: _____

Contact info: _____

Name: _____

Contact info: _____

# DAY 27 - MY THOUGHTS

If you only walk on sunny days, you will never reach
your destination.

- Aleph Paulo Coelho -

_____

_____

_____

_____

_____

_____

_____

_____

_____

_____

# DAY 27 - MINDFULNESS MINUTE

Make this page your second attempt at a gratitude list.
Has what you were grateful for before you embarked on
your journey changed since you have been traveling?

_____

_____

_____

_____

_____

_____

_____

_____

_____

_____

_____

_____

# DAY 28

# DAY 28 - MY CAMINO

From: _____ to: _____

The weather is:                    I am feeling:

☀ ☁ ⛅ 🌧 ❄          ☺ 😄 😐 🙁 😴

➡ ➡ ➡ ➡ ➡ ➡ ➡ ➡ ➡ ➡ ➡ ➡ ➡

Total distance traveled: ____ KMs ☐ Miles ☐ Inches ☐
  Walked ☐ Cycled ☐ Taxi ☐ Bus ☐ Plane ☐ Horse ☐
  Other ☐ _____

➡ ➡ ➡ ➡ ➡ ➡ ➡ ➡ ➡ ➡ ➡ ➡ ➡

Stayed @: _____
Albergue ☐ Hostel ☐ Hotel ☐ Tent ☐ Under the stars ☐

➡ ➡ ➡ ➡ ➡ ➡ ➡ ➡ ➡ ➡ ➡ ➡ ➡

Ate: Breakfast ☐ _____
          Eat it again! ☐ So So ☐ Bleck ☐
       Lunch ☐ _____
          Eat it again! ☐ So So ☐ Bleck ☐
      Dinner ☐ _____
          Eat it again! ☐ So So ☐ Bleck ☐

Spent: _____ Euros ☐ Dollars ☐ Other ☐
On lodgings ☐ On food ☐ On Gifts ☐ Other ☐

➡ ➡ ➡ ➡ ➡ ➡ ➡ ➡ ➡ ➡ ➡ ➡ ➡

Tomorrow is a new day. Important things to remember:

_____
_____
_____

# DAY 28 - MY PURPOSE

What is my purpose today? ♡

_____
_____
_____

Who am I to help? 🤝 With what?

_____
_____
_____

Who will help me? 🤝 With what?

_____
_____
_____

Lessons learned along The Way
Gifts from the Universe/GOD/Angels/Spirits

**1** _____

**2** _____

**3** _____

What piece of equipment am I most grateful for today?

_____

Angels (Pilgrims) I met on the Camino today:

Name: _____

Contact info: _____

Name: _____

Contact info: _____

## DAY 28 - MY THOUGHTS

The soul that sees beauty may sometimes walk alone.
- Johann Wolfgang von Goethe -

_____

_____

_____

_____

_____

_____

_____

_____

_____

_____

_____

# DAY 28 - MINDFULNESS MINUTE

Art Project: Sketch, doodle or draw the item or items
that are closest to you at this very moment?

Don't forget that this is your journal so it does not
have to be perfect, and no one has to see it.

# DAY 29

# DAY 29 - MY CAMINO

From: _____ to: _____

The weather is:                  I am feeling:

☀ ☁ ⛅ 🌧 ❄          ☺ 😃 😐 😫 😴

➡ ➡ ➡ ➡ ➡ ➡ ➡ ➡ ➡ ➡ ➡ ➡ ➡

Total distance traveled: ___ KMs ☐ Miles ☐ Inches ☐

Walked ☐ Cycled ☐ Taxi ☐ Bus ☐ Plane ☐ Horse ☐
Other ☐ _____

➡ ➡ ➡ ➡ ➡ ➡ ➡ ➡ ➡ ➡ ➡ ➡ ➡

Stayed @: _____

Albergue ☐ Hostel ☐ Hotel ☐ Tent ☐ Under the stars ☐

➡ ➡ ➡ ➡ ➡ ➡ ➡ ➡ ➡ ➡ ➡ ➡ ➡

Ate:  Breakfast ☐ _____

Eat it again! ☐  So So ☐  Bleck ☐
Lunch ☐ _____

Eat it again! ☐  So So ☐  Bleck ☐
Dinner ☐ _____

Eat it again! ☐  So So ☐  Bleck ☐

Spent: _____ Euros ☐  Dollars ☐  Other ☐
On lodgings ☐  On food ☐  On Gifts ☐  Other ☐

➡ ➡ ➡ ➡ ➡ ➡ ➡ ➡ ➡ ➡ ➡ ➡ ➡

Tomorrow is a new day. Important things to remember:

_____

_____

_____

# DAY 29 - MY PURPOSE

What is my purpose today? ♡

_____
_____
_____

Who am I to help? 🤝 With what?

_____
_____
_____

Who will help me? 🤝 With what?

_____
_____
_____

Lessons learned along The Way
Gifts from the Universe/GOD/Angels/Spirits

**1** _____

**2** _____

**3** _____

What piece of equipment am I most grateful for today?

_____

Angels (Pilgrims) I met on the Camino today:

Name: _____

Contact info: _____

Name: _____

Contact info: _____

Walking is Man's best medicine.
- Hippocrates -

_____

_____

_____

_____

_____

_____

_____

_____

_____

_____

_____

_____

## DAY 29 - MINDFULNESS MINUTE

Reflect: Take a moment and look back on how far you have come and how you have changed as a person.

_____

_____

_____

_____

_____

_____

_____

_____

_____

_____

_____

No obvious changes?
How have you become stronger?

# DAY 30

# DAY 30 - MY CAMINO

From: _____ to: _____

The weather is:      I am feeling:

☀ ☁ ⛅ 🌧 🌨     ☺ 😄 😐 😣 😴

➡ ➡ ➡ ➡ ➡ ➡ ➡ ➡ ➡ ➡ ➡ ➡ ➡

Total distance traveled: ___ KMs ☐ Miles ☐ Inches ☐

Walked ☐ Cycled ☐ Taxi ☐ Bus ☐ Plane ☐ Horse ☐
Other ☐ _____

➡ ➡ ➡ ➡ ➡ ➡ ➡ ➡ ➡ ➡ ➡ ➡ ➡

Stayed @: _____

Albergue ☐ Hostel ☐ Hotel ☐ Tent ☐ Under the stars ☐

➡ ➡ ➡ ➡ ➡ ➡ ➡ ➡ ➡ ➡ ➡ ➡ ➡

Ate: Breakfast ☐ _____

         Eat it again! ☐ So So ☐ Bleck ☐

     Lunch ☐ _____

         Eat it again! ☐ So So ☐ Bleck ☐

     Dinner ☐ _____

         Eat it again! ☐ So So ☐ Bleck ☐

Spent: _____ Euros ☐ Dollars ☐ Other ☐
On lodgings ☐ On food ☐ On Gifts ☐ Other ☐

➡ ➡ ➡ ➡ ➡ ➡ ➡ ➡ ➡ ➡ ➡ ➡ ➡

Tomorrow is a new day. Important things to remember:

_____

_____

_____

# DAY 30 - MY PURPOSE

What is my purpose today? ♡

_____
_____
_____

Who am I to help? 🤝 With what?

_____
_____
_____

Who will help me? 🤝 With what?

_____
_____
_____

Lessons learned along The Way
Gifts from the Universe/GOD/Angels/Spirits

**1** _____

**2** _____

**3** _____

What piece of equipment am I most grateful for today?

_____

Angels (Pilgrims) I met on the Camino today:

Name: _____

Contact info: _____

Name: _____

Contact info: _____

## DAY 30 - MY THOUGHTS

The miracle isn't that I finished. The miracle is that I
had the courage to start.
- John Bingham -

_____

_____

_____

_____

_____

_____

_____

_____

_____

_____

# DAY 30 - MINDFULNESS MINUTE

The Camino Promise: There is a well-known promise
that the Camino makes to all who travel along the path.
It promises to provide.

_____

_____

_____

_____

_____

_____

_____

_____

_____

_____

_____

How and what has the Camino provided for you?

# DAY 31

From: _____ to: _____

The weather is:                    I am feeling:

☀ ☁ ⛅ 🌧 ❄        ☺ 😀 😐 ☹ 😴

➡ ➡ ➡ ➡ ➡ ➡ ➡ ➡ ➡ ➡ ➡ ➡ ➡

Total distance traveled: ___ KMs ☐ Miles ☐ Inches ☐

Walked ☐ Cycled ☐ Taxi ☐ Bus ☐ Plane ☐ Horse ☐
Other ☐ _____

➡ ➡ ➡ ➡ ➡ ➡ ➡ ➡ ➡ ➡ ➡ ➡ ➡

Stayed @: _____

Albergue ☐ Hostel ☐ Hotel ☐ Tent ☐ Under the stars ☐

➡ ➡ ➡ ➡ ➡ ➡ ➡ ➡ ➡ ➡ ➡ ➡ ➡

Ate:  Breakfast ☐ _____

                 Eat it again! ☐  So So ☐  Bleck ☐
          Lunch ☐ _____

                 Eat it again! ☐  So So ☐  Bleck ☐
         Dinner ☐ _____

                 Eat it again! ☐  So So ☐  Bleck ☐

Spent: _____ Euros ☐  Dollars ☐  Other ☐
On lodgings ☐  On food ☐  On Gifts ☐  Other ☐

➡ ➡ ➡ ➡ ➡ ➡ ➡ ➡ ➡ ➡ ➡ ➡ ➡

Tomorrow is a new day. Important things to remember:

_____

_____

_____

# DAY 31 - MY PURPOSE

What is my purpose today? ♡

_____
_____
_____

Who am I to help? 🤝 With what?

_____
_____
_____

Who will help me? 🤝 With what?

_____
_____
_____

Lessons learned along The Way
Gifts from the Universe/GOD/Angels/Spirits

**1** _____

**2** _____

**3** _____

What piece of equipment am I most grateful for today?

_____

Angels (Pilgrims) I met on the Camino today:

Name: _____

Contact info: _____

Name: _____

Contact info: _____

# DAY 31 - MY THOUGHTS

We grow fearless by walking into our fears.
- Robin Sharma -

# DAY 31 - MINDFULNESS MINUTE

Magical Mystery: Did you witness any miracles on the path?

_____

_____

_____

_____

_____

_____

_____

_____

_____

_____

I believe in miracles, so nothing will surprise me.

# DAY 32

# DAY 32 - MY CAMINO

From: _____ to: _____

The weather is:                 I am feeling:

☀ ☁ ⛅ 🌧 🌨            ☺ 😄 😐 😣 😴

➡ ➡ ➡ ➡ ➡ ➡ ➡ ➡ ➡ ➡ ➡ ➡ ➡

Total distance traveled: ___ KMs ☐ Miles ☐ Inches ☐

Walked ☐ Cycled ☐ Taxi ☐ Bus ☐ Plane ☐ Horse ☐
Other ☐ _____

➡ ➡ ➡ ➡ ➡ ➡ ➡ ➡ ➡ ➡ ➡ ➡ ➡

Stayed @: _____

Albergue ☐ Hostel ☐ Hotel ☐ Tent ☐ Under the stars ☐

➡ ➡ ➡ ➡ ➡ ➡ ➡ ➡ ➡ ➡ ➡ ➡ ➡

Ate: Breakfast ☐ _____

          Eat it again! ☐ So So ☐ Bleck ☐
       Lunch ☐ _____

          Eat it again! ☐ So So ☐ Bleck ☐
     Dinner ☐ _____

          Eat it again! ☐ So So ☐ Bleck ☐

Spent: _____ Euros ☐ Dollars ☐ Other ☐
On lodgings ☐ On food ☐ On Gifts ☐ Other ☐

➡ ➡ ➡ ➡ ➡ ➡ ➡ ➡ ➡ ➡ ➡ ➡ ➡

Tomorrow is a new day. Important things to remember:

_____

_____

_____

What is my purpose today? ♡

_____
_____
_____

Who am I to help? 🤝 With what?

_____
_____
_____

Who will help me? 🤝 With what?

_____
_____
_____

Lessons learned along The Way
Gifts from the Universe/GOD/Angels/Spirits

**1** _____

**2** _____

**3** _____

What piece of equipment am I most grateful for today?

_____

Angels (Pilgrims) I met on the Camino today:

Name: _____

Contact info: _____

Name: _____

Contact info: _____

# DAY 32 - MY THOUGHTS

The best way to lengthen out our days, is to walk
steadily and with purpose.
                    - Charles Dickens -

_____

_____

_____

_____

_____

_____

_____

_____

_____

_____

_____

# DAY 32 - MINDFULNESS MINUTE

Feel the Feels: Write about the days which had the highest or lowest emotions.

_____

_____

_____

_____

_____

_____

_____

_____

_____

_____

_____

Were there days where you wanted to
throw in the towel and go home?

# DAY 33

From: _____ to: _____

The weather is:               I am feeling:

☀ ☁ ⛅ 🌦 🌨          ☺ 😄 😐 😣 😴

➡ ➡ ➡ ➡ ➡ ➡ ➡ ➡ ➡ ➡ ➡ ➡ ➡ ➡

Total distance traveled: ___ KMs ☐ Miles ☐ Inches ☐

Walked ☐ Cycled ☐ Taxi ☐ Bus ☐ Plane ☐ Horse ☐
Other ☐ _____

➡ ➡ ➡ ➡ ➡ ➡ ➡ ➡ ➡ ➡ ➡ ➡ ➡ ➡

Stayed @: _____

Albergue ☐ Hostel ☐ Hotel ☐ Tent ☐ Under the stars ☐

➡ ➡ ➡ ➡ ➡ ➡ ➡ ➡ ➡ ➡ ➡ ➡ ➡ ➡

Ate: Breakfast ☐ _____

　　　　　　Eat it again! ☐  So So ☐  Bleck ☐
　　　Lunch ☐ _____

　　　　　　Eat it again! ☐  So So ☐  Bleck ☐
　　　Dinner ☐ _____

　　　　　　Eat it again! ☐  So So ☐  Bleck ☐

Spent: _____ Euros ☐  Dollars ☐  Other ☐
On lodgings ☐  On food ☐  On Gifts ☐  Other ☐

➡ ➡ ➡ ➡ ➡ ➡ ➡ ➡ ➡ ➡ ➡ ➡ ➡ ➡

Tomorrow is a new day. Important things to remember:

_____

_____

_____

# DAY 33 - MY PURPOSE

What is my purpose today? ♡

_____
_____
_____

Who am I to help? 🤝 With what?

_____
_____
_____

Who will help me? 🤝 With what?

_____
_____
_____

Lessons learned along The Way
Gifts from the Universe/GOD/Angels/Spirits

**1** _____

**2** _____

**3** _____

What piece of equipment am I most grateful for today?

_____

Angels (Pilgrims) I met on the Camino today:

Name: _____

Contact info: _____

Name: _____

Contact info: _____

As people are walking all the time, in the same spot, a
path appears.

- John Locke -

_____

_____

_____

_____

_____

_____

_____

_____

_____

_____

# DAY 33 - MINDFULNESS MINUTE

Safe Space: Write your heart out! Tell a story.

Ready, get set, GO!

_____

_____

_____

_____

_____

_____

_____

_____

_____

_____

_____

_____

# DAY 34

# DAY 34 - MY CAMINO

From: _____ to: _____

The weather is:                    I am feeling:

☼  ☁  ⛅  🌧  🌨          ☺  😃  😐  😔  😴

➡ ➡ ➡ ➡ ➡ ➡ ➡ ➡ ➡ ➡ ➡ ➡ ➡

Total distance traveled: ___ KMs ☐ Miles ☐ Inches ☐

Walked ☐ Cycled ☐ Taxi ☐ Bus ☐ Plane ☐ Horse ☐
Other ☐ _____

➡ ➡ ➡ ➡ ➡ ➡ ➡ ➡ ➡ ➡ ➡ ➡ ➡

Stayed @: _____

Albergue ☐ Hostel ☐ Hotel ☐ Tent ☐ Under the stars ☐

➡ ➡ ➡ ➡ ➡ ➡ ➡ ➡ ➡ ➡ ➡ ➡ ➡

Ate:  Breakfast ☐ _____

               Eat it again! ☐  So So ☐  Bleck ☐
       Lunch ☐ _____

               Eat it again! ☐  So So ☐  Bleck ☐
       Dinner ☐ _____

               Eat it again! ☐  So So ☐  Bleck ☐

Spent: _____ Euros ☐  Dollars ☐  Other ☐
On lodgings ☐  On food ☐  On Gifts ☐  Other ☐

➡ ➡ ➡ ➡ ➡ ➡ ➡ ➡ ➡ ➡ ➡ ➡ ➡

Tomorrow is a new day. Important things to remember:

_____

_____

_____

# DAY 34 - MY PURPOSE

What is my purpose today? ♡

_____
_____
_____

Who am I to help? 🤝 With what?

_____
_____
_____

Who will help me? 🤝 With what?

_____
_____
_____

Lessons learned along The Way
Gifts from the Universe/GOD/Angels/Spirits

**1** _____

**2** _____

**3** _____

What piece of equipment am I most grateful for today?

_____

Angels (Pilgrims) I met on the Camino today:

Name: _____

Contact info: _____

Name: _____

Contact info: _____

## DAY 34 - MY THOUGHTS

Ask a total stranger for their favorite quote.

_____

_____

_____

_____

_____

_____

_____

_____

_____

_____

_____

# DAY 34 - MINDFULNESS MINUTE

Crystal Ball: How do you think your life will be different when you return home from the Camino?

_____

_____

_____

_____

_____

_____

_____

_____

_____

_____

Are there any changes you want to make?
Will your life be the same?

# DAY 35

From: _____ to: _____

The weather is:                    I am feeling:

☼  ☁  ⛅  🌧  ❄                    ☺  😀  😐  😣  😴

➡ ➡ ➡ ➡ ➡ ➡ ➡ ➡ ➡ ➡ ➡ ➡ ➡ ➡ ➡

Total distance traveled: ____ KMs ☐ Miles ☐ Inches ☐

Walked ☐ Cycled ☐ Taxi ☐ Bus ☐ Plane ☐ Horse ☐
Other ☐ _____

➡ ➡ ➡ ➡ ➡ ➡ ➡ ➡ ➡ ➡ ➡ ➡ ➡ ➡ ➡

Stayed @: _____

Albergue ☐ Hostel ☐ Hotel ☐ Tent ☐ Under the stars ☐

➡ ➡ ➡ ➡ ➡ ➡ ➡ ➡ ➡ ➡ ➡ ➡ ➡ ➡ ➡

Ate:  Breakfast ☐ _____

　　　　　　　Eat it again! ☐  So So ☐  Bleck ☐

　　　　Lunch ☐ _____

　　　　　　　Eat it again! ☐  So So ☐  Bleck ☐

　　　Dinner ☐ _____

　　　　　　　Eat it again! ☐  So So ☐  Bleck ☐

Spent: _____ Euros ☐  Dollars ☐  Other ☐
On lodgings ☐  On food ☐  On Gifts ☐  Other ☐

➡ ➡ ➡ ➡ ➡ ➡ ➡ ➡ ➡ ➡ ➡ ➡ ➡ ➡ ➡

Tomorrow is a new day. Important things to remember:

_____

_____

_____

# DAY 35 - MY PURPOSE

What is my purpose today? ♡

_____

_____

_____

Who am I to help? 🤝 With what?

_____

_____

_____

Who will help me? 🤝 With what?

_____

_____

_____

Lessons learned along The Way
Gifts from the Universe/GOD/Angels/Spirits

**1** _____

**2** _____

**3** _____

What piece of equipment am I most grateful for today?

_____

Angels (Pilgrims) I met on the Camino today:

Name: _____

Contact info: _____

Name: _____

Contact info: _____

Ask someone you know for their favorite quote.

_____

_____

_____

_____

_____

_____

_____

_____

_____

_____

_____

# DAY 35 - MINDFULNESS MINUTE

Social Experiment: Ask someone you are traveling with
or someone you have just met to write what it has been
like to travel with you.

_____

_____

_____

_____

_____

_____

_____

_____

_____

_____

_____

Ask them to be honest... and kind.

# DAY 36

# DAY 36 - MY CAMINO

From: _____ to: _____

The weather is:                I am feeling:

☀ ☁ ⛅ 🌧 🌨          ☺ 😄 😐 😣 😴

➡ ➡ ➡ ➡ ➡ ➡ ➡ ➡ ➡ ➡ ➡ ➡ ➡

Total distance traveled: ___ KMs ☐ Miles ☐ Inches ☐

Walked ☐ Cycled ☐ Taxi ☐ Bus ☐ Plane ☐ Horse ☐
Other ☐ _____

➡ ➡ ➡ ➡ ➡ ➡ ➡ ➡ ➡ ➡ ➡ ➡ ➡

Stayed @: _____

Albergue ☐ Hostel ☐ Hotel ☐ Tent ☐ Under the stars ☐

➡ ➡ ➡ ➡ ➡ ➡ ➡ ➡ ➡ ➡ ➡ ➡

Ate: Breakfast ☐ _____

Eat it again! ☐ So So ☐ Bleck ☐

Lunch ☐ _____

Eat it again! ☐ So So ☐ Bleck ☐

Dinner ☐ _____

Eat it again! ☐ So So ☐ Bleck ☐

Spent: _____ Euros ☐ Dollars ☐ Other ☐
On lodgings ☐ On food ☐ On Gifts ☐ Other ☐

➡ ➡ ➡ ➡ ➡ ➡ ➡ ➡ ➡ ➡ ➡ ➡ ➡

Tomorrow is a new day. Important things to remember:

_____

_____

_____

# DAY 36 - MY PURPOSE

What is my purpose today? ♡

_____

_____

_____

Who am I to help? 🤝 With what?

_____

_____

_____

Who will help me? 🤝 With what?

_____

_____

_____

Lessons learned along The Way
Gifts from the Universe/GOD/Angels/Spirits

**1** _____

**2** _____

**3** _____

What piece of equipment am I most grateful for today?

_____

Angels (Pilgrims) I met on the Camino today:

Name: _____

Contact info: _____

Name: _____

Contact info: _____

## DAY 36 - MY THOUGHTS

Your favorite quote.

_____

_____

_____

_____

_____

_____

_____

_____

_____

_____

_____

# DAY 36 - MINDFULNESS MINUTE

On the Edge: On the last night before completing your
journey, write about how it will feel to be finished. You
are now on the edge of completing your adventure.

_____

_____

_____

_____

_____

_____

_____

_____

_____

_____

Is there anything you need to leave in Spain?
Physically or spiritually.

# EXTRA NOTES

_____

_____

_____

_____

_____

_____

_____

_____

_____

_____

_____

_____

_____

_____

_____

_____

_____

_____

_____

_____

_____

_____

_____

_____

# CONGRATULATIONS!
## You made it!

My Camino completion date:

_____

Proposed Camino return date:

_____

You ALREADY know that you want to!

# THANKS TO...

Mammut hiking boots for making my awesome turquoise boots. Please note: No boots were harmed in the making of this journal.

Quotes: All the famous people who have inspired us with such wonderful and meaningful quotes that we can apply to any part of our lives.

And finally, special thanks go out to Aprille, Karen, Joe, and Randi-Mae, for their love, support, inspiration, keen eyes, and artistic touch.

# ABOUT THE AUTHOR

*My Camino Journal* is Heather Gailey's very first publishing adventure.

It is a journal that is unique in that it was designed to provide a non-denominational, meditative, and spiritual writing space for those who choose to physically traverse the Camino de Santiago through Spain as well as other popular Camino journeys.

It provides a 36-day recurring structure for those who have never journaled before or for those who may tend to experience blank page phobia.

This funky journal has specific space to document daily adventures, and collect the contact information of fellow pilgrims. It gives you room to ruminate on important spiritual teaching and learnings, and provides many thoughtful prompts and quotes to assist with the discovery of an inner journey to Santiago and to Self. A precious keepsake of your journey you will have forever.

Heather Gailey is a victim advocate and adult educator by day and a mixed media artist in every other available corner of her life. She makes her home just outside of Toronto, Canada.

Every chance she gets she teaches Art Journaling and speaks to groups who want to hear about her...

## Best CAMINO STORY EVER!

# Travel
# Sleep
# Wake
# Eat
# Walk
# Eat
# Sleep
# Repeat